MENTAL HEALTH IN CHILDHOOD

MENTAL HEALTH
IN CHILDHOOD

by

CHARLES L. C. BURNS

FIDES PUBLISHERS ASSOCIATION

CHICAGO 19, ILLINOIS

Library of Congress Catalog Card Number: 56-11627

Copyright: 1956, Fides Publishers
Association, Chicago,
Illinois

Nihil Obstat: Paul Bailey, C.S.C.,
University of Notre Dame

Imprimatur: Leo A. Pursley, D.D., Apostolic
Administrator of the Diocese of Fort
Wayne, Indiana

Manufactured by American Book–Stratford Press
75 Varick St., New York, New York

 55

Contents

Preface

"Man has a natural urge towards complete goodness."
St. Thomas Aquinas, *Disputations*.

This is to be a short book, chiefly for the reason that, in my experience, longer books on this subject go largely unread; people have no longer the time nor the patience.

It is written from the conviction that we now possess a body of knowledge and experience in the psychology of childhood which is profoundly and inevitably affecting our views on the upbringing, education, and treatment of children. The extent and influence of this knowledge is, however, still far from being realized and appreciated, especially among those whose values and traditions are very fixed and apparently secure. These tend to look upon it with suspicion, whilst others take to it with undue enthusiasm and well-meant misunderstanding in its application.

I would only claim two things for the brief book that follows: one, that it is free from technical words and phrases, commonly called jargon, and secondly, that it is based on more than twenty years of practical experience in dealing with maladjusted, nervous, and delinquent children.

My object in writing it is to put forward certain facts, reflections, and ideas, on varied aspects of my work. We are all indeed "concerned" with the subject of maladjusted children, and with the goal of mental health in childhood. What I have to say may be of some practical use to those who deal with these children, but it is meant to be more in the nature of a brief descriptive introduction to the subject, for any intelligent person to read. It applies in the main to children who come within the school system of the State, and refers to organizations and institutions which are established for their benefit. It is hoped also that it will help parents to bring up children, and teachers to deal with their problem children.

If I write, naturally, mainly as a psychiatrist, I do so in addition as a parent and as an ordinary citizen; therefore I can express views, and perhaps prejudices, in the latter capacities, which range beyond the strictly professional field of work.

It will be obvious, from internal evidence, that this book is written by a Catholic, and addressed to some extent to his fellow Catholics. This however does not mean that it cannot be usefully read by others; because the matters discussed are not dependent on any religious formulation, though I believe they are based on Christian values. In the domain of child psychology we share ideals and values with the humanists, whose ideas derive in fact from the Christian ethic: we believe in the love of our neighbor, we believe in the freedom of the individual conscience, and the respect due to the human person. (In the Marxian belief this principle is transferred to the Collectivity—in practice to the Communist *élite*—and this belief cannot therefore accept "Western" psychology, which is not, as yet, altogether materialist.)

It is true that modern psychology, and its application, for example in "Child Guidance", meets with less understanding and acceptance among Catholics than others. This is understandable, firstly, because we are traditionalists, and take time—sometimes a little too much time—to assimilate and extract what is good from new ideas and movements. Secondly because we are naturally and often justly suspicious of "progressive" movements, which may be exaggerated in their claims, and prove to be yet another will-o'-the-wisp in mankind's search for happiness.

There are certain aspects of human nature which are stressed by Catholics in the application of psychological principles. Some ideas are rejected or modified, others affirmed. In Catholic belief we recognize sin and moral responsibility as well as psychological conditioning. We stress authority and obedience more than the pure humanist, who tends to be utopian or idealist in his views about the "natural" goodness of man. However far we may push the natural explanation of behavior, in terms of heredity and environment, we have room for freedom of choice and responsibility. Sin and real guilt, as opposed to a morbid feeling of guilt, are not invented by theologians: they are facts in human nature.

Now Catholics are divided like the rest of mankind into the "tough" and "tender"—as William James described these two main types of people. They are as varied in their political, psychological, or artistic beliefs as anybody else. But the danger is that the "tough" may be more vocal and more powerful, or that a defensive, suspicious attitude may be set up against anything new. The answer given may be that in religion alone lies the solution to all human prob-

lems. Ultimately it does, of course; but there is a wide
field in the natural sphere which has to be tilled for
the fulfilment and enrichment of life. Nature has to be
nurtured to be receptive of Grace. As the Catholic
Belgian psychiatrist De Greeff puts it, there is too wide
a gap between Man and the perfection of Doctrine:
"It would seem necessary," he says, "to introduce between man and doctrine a way of feeling, a kind of
social pedagogic, which prepares the human being to
give real value to his Christianity." [1]

The need for understanding, tolerance, and tenderness is a desperate one in our days; we cannot afford,
any of us, to have rigid, puritanical, or punitive ideas
with regard to human relationships. We need a deep
human pity as well as a belief in the infinite mercy of
God. There is danger in too much rectitude; in that
kind of cold "charity" which finds it necessary to *force*
children to be good, to be obedient, to be religious:
with no real understanding, no warmth, no sympathy.
It is terrible when sensitive children are punished or
shamed, unjustly or stupidly, often from sheer lack of
imagination.

If this book is aimed at anyone in particular, it is
at those men and women, lay and religious, who are
dealing with deprived, delinquent and maladjusted
children, in schools and institutions of all kinds. I hope
however that it may arouse a social and psychological
conscience in others, who should not allow these children to remain isolated as it were in the midst of them,
but take an interest, if not an active share, in their
welfare.

[1] In *Notre Destinée et Nos Instincts*, 1945, Plon, Paris, p. 132. (Author's tr.).

1

Maladjusted Children

In the ordinary way we recognize that some children are so badly behaved, or so nervous, as to constitute problems which cannot be settled by any ordinary means of correction or treatment, at home or at school. The symptoms of maladjustment are extremely variable: they range from violent tempers, aggressive acts, destructiveness, and stealing at one end of the scale, to timidity, fears, enuresis (bed-wetting), insomnia, and vague physical symptoms on the other. All children, of course, go through phases, both of difficult behavior and nervousness; they would hardly be "normal" if they did not; it is only when such manifestations are extreme and prolonged that they deserve the name of maladjustment.

Apart from the trouble or unhappiness caused by these children in the present, we have to realize that from their ranks will come many of the neurotics and delinquents of the future, so from all points of view any help that we can give them will be amply repaid. The adult neurotic is to some extent the child of the past, and repeats in many ways the patterns of feeling and behavior of his childhood.

We have next to enquire whence come the psychological disturbances, the "maladjustments", of childhood. How far are they due to heredity, how far to the present environment and how far to that of the early years? These all play a part in varying degrees of importance, in every case.

The physical type or temperament is a matter of inheritance: some children are by nature excitable or restless; some bold and some timid; some have a more sensitive nervous system than others. There may be tendencies in families which produce behavior of an epileptic or explosive type, which is shown in the actual tracing of electrical waves in the brain; or else a strain of neurosis or insanity. But these tendencies are given and to a large extent fixed; whereas the environment can be altered, and the effects of the early environment modified by treatment, as we shall see.

The elements of the *present* environment are many and various, ranging from bad housing conditions to strain at school, from too little care at home to too much, from spoiling to neglect or harshness. A large number of the less serious problems, and some of the apparently serious, are dependent on such factors, which can be modified with the use of common sense aided by a knowledge of psychology.

Of greater interest are the more intangible elements which shape the human personality: the interplay of the instincts and emotions as they develop and change from infancy onwards. Here we meet the deep levels of the unconscious mind, the foreshadowing of the child's future being. We meet with the primal emotions of love and hate, of aggression and jealousy: their satisfaction, resolution, or frustration. To understand and be able to treat each particular case, we have to acquire a thorough and detailed history of the past as well as a clear picture of the present. We need to know about the personality and upbringing of the parents, the circumstances of birth and infancy, the illnesses and separations in the history of the child; his relationships at all ages to different members of the family. Particularly the exact age and circumstances when problems were first shown.

Since we cannot enter into all these details, it may serve as a practical illustration to take one of the commonest and most powerful emotions which may set off a problem of maladjustment (although the seeds of it may have been sown even earlier), namely jealousy.

It is quite often found that the beginnings of maladjusted behavior coincide with the birth of a brother or sister. This is more likely in small families, where there may be a gap of several years between one and the other. Jealousy may be expressed openly, by attacks upon the hated (and loved) rival, but it may also be shown indirectly, i.e. unconsciously, in a variety of ways. It may appear as regression to baby ways: enuresis, fear of the dark, dependence, or naughtiness; as though the presence of the new baby reawakened infantile feelings. In some cases it has an effect on the whole personality; the child becomes less bright, less responsive. It is as though the loss, or fancied loss, of much of the love and attention which he had hitherto received, had diminished his stature, or extinguished the brightness within.

The effects may indeed be dramatic, as shown in the following cases: *Bob,* aged eleven, was brought to a Clinic for enuresis and encopresis (soiling). This had started four years previously, following the birth of a sister. The mother was in hospital and Bob went to his grandmother's. When he returned home he found a new baby, and felt that his mother was impatient with him. He not only regressed in habits, but became lethargic and indifferent. Although intelligent, he failed to pass the examination for higher education. His play at the Clinic helped him to work off the explosive resentment and aggression which he had suppressed. The incontinence cleared up, but it has taken him long to settle down to any activity or interest in work or play.

Dick, aged eight, was brought for attacks of nervous asthma and fear of school. These had started three years ago, soon after the birth of a baby brother. Though he had been prepared for the new arrival, he was upset when he was sent off to his grandparents, where he had to sleep for the first time on his own; he screamed and had nightmares. There was also, in this case, some jealousy of the father, who had come home from the war when Dick was aged two. There was no history of asthma in the family. The parents were kind and sensible. Dick seemed depressed and weedy; he was afraid of school because he had missed so much. He was openly jealous of the brother, who could go out shopping with mother while he had to go to school.

The asthma came on mostly after the holidays. With treatment at the Clinic, and advice to the parents, his complaint gradually passed off.

These examples show how the seeds of jealousy laid down many years before can produce bitter fruit later. So, too, other emotional hurts can continue to influence outlook and behavior. The child who at puberty starts to become rebellious, or who starts stealing, may be found to have suffered a hurt when quite small. He may have suffered rejection or separation at a time when it was bitterly felt, but understood only in terms of fantasy: of abandonment by wicked people: parents whom he could no longer trust.

It may seem unjust that the formation of the personality should be thus bound up with the old unhappy things of long ago, but so it is; such is the human state. There are, however, many possibilities of adjustment; the early influences are overcome by later and more satisfactory experiences. But in cases of neurosis, this somehow has not happened, or else later events have reactivated these early emotional attitudes. Moreover, as has been said, we now have a good foundation of that knowledge and skill whereby we may undo what seems like an evil destiny. We can make the child aware of how these early feelings and fantasies are working within him to create a false situation, which can be overcome by this deeper understanding. The therapist shows him that there are other possible relationships of a positive kind. It is a kind of purgation of the emotions, so that bad feelings are replaced by good.

Besides this particular therapeutic process, other

means are employed to ease strain, and to open up possibilities for a healthy and creative outlook. The description of this process of healing is taken up in the next chapter.

INSTABILITY

The following is a type of case which is likely to provide a great deal of trouble and sorrow to parents, a problem to teachers, and an expense to the State. The boy concerned is typical of several others, who have been "carried" at a Child-Guidance Clinic for several years. They may be described as the "unstable" type.

Tony was aged eight when first sent to the Clinic seven years ago for being difficult to manage, stealing and truanting, inattentive and disturbing at school. (Some people would at once say: "All he needs is a good thrashing.") He was adopted at the age of two weeks by a decent, rather elderly couple who have tended to over-protect him. He has always been fidgety and backward. At school he is not considered mentally defective but he is excitable, has no powers of concentration, no idea of conduct. He is uninfluenced by punishment.

Now, in such a case it could be said from the beginning that he would prove a very difficult case for years to come. His E.E.G. (electrical brain test) was abnormal and still is. His intelligence was just over the border-line for educationally subnormal children.

He improved while under attendance at the Clinic; later on, when in trouble again for stealing, he was sent to a residential school for maladjusted children with further improvement.

His father died when he was aged thirteen, which gradually created a tense situation with his mother. Now at puberty he has left school but cannot settle to any job; his mother is afraid of his violence, and he will have to be sent away for treatment to a mental hospital for adolescents. Here he will receive treatment with endocrine glands, as well as being rehabilitated socially, and trained to some suitable job. His future is uncertain but there is a chance that with full adolescence he may mature and find some useful place in society.

Here then we have a case with a combination of handicaps of every sort: he has inherited an unstable nervous system and dull intelligence; he is adopted by parents who have not experienced having children of their own, who have become too protective and are not sufficiently firm. He loses his "father" just at an age which most needs male support.

After constant supervision and guidance, he improves, but relapses because he lacks the necessary stability and because his controlling inner force—call it super-ego, or conscience—is so rudimentary and immature. He, and his parent, will need constant expert support and advice if the boy is to make anything of his life. There are many like him who, if not helped, may swell the ranks of the retrogrades, the outcasts, or the chronic mentally sick. We need special institutions for these types, which we have not got as yet. It is however necessary that school teachers should be able to recognize this type of boy; not expecting too much from him, keeping him going, seeking expert help before it is too late.

DEPRIVED CHILDREN

It will be evident what disastrous consequences may also result from the separation from, or death of, one of the parents at a critical time in a child's life. Often however the child will adopt a "father-figure" or "mother-substitute", and work through to a satisfactory adjustment. In this and many other situations we find indeed that where the ego or personality is strong, the child can survive unscathed and even be strengthened by events that may be disastrous for those who are predisposed to neurosis, whose defences give way and can only with difficulty be built up. *The resilience and adaptability of children is one of their most precious endowments.*

If it is accepted that the development of a child into a normal human being depends upon the conditions for natural development, and, above all, upon the relationship with a mother in the earliest years, this should have important implications for the care of deprived children: those who have been deprived of normal home life.

Orphaned, abandoned or neglected children have to be placed in large institutions, because that is the only provision available in many places, and however devoted may be the care provided there, the small child cannot find the individual affection which he needs. Others of these children are placed in foster-homes where they may fail to adjust themselves, and are moved from one to another; others are separated for long periods from their families and lose touch with them.

There is now a considerable amount of evidence to show the possible effects of such deprivation or separation. It has been demonstrated by observers in America, and illustrated by actual films and graphs, how the development of babies in a Home where they received adequate physical care but no personal affection, was slowed down in every respect and almost arrested, month by month; they were emotionally starved.

It has been shown that a large proportion of adult asocial or so-called psychopathic individuals have been deprived of all adequate maternal care in the first two years of life. They have grown up unable to form any real human relationships because they have missed the vital link with society: the mother. Also, in the case of many antisocial or criminal types, there has been an initial bond with a mother, which has been violently broken by rejection or separation at an early age, and has inflicted a fatal injury to the personality. Some of these unfortunates fail to respond to any attempt at reformation and therapy.

There is remarkable unanimity among workers in all countries where such observations have been carried out. It is possible that they have been so impressed by these results that too pessimistic an impression has been produced, and inadequate allowance made for the powers of compensation and recuperation shown by individuals. Nevertheless these facts are already having considerable effect in many ways. Homes for children are being organized in smaller units, approximating as much as possible to large families, and those who are responsible for their care are being trained in the principles of mental health. There is a tendency to avoid taking children away from home for any but the most urgent reasons, so that it is almost a slogan that "a bad parent is better than no parent". Unfortunately, however, the corollary that these bad, careless, or stupid parents must be given help and training, and not just left to neglect their children, is not so often acted upon.

It is being recognized that to separate infants from their mothers during lying-in is wrong and unscientific; there is a return to what is called in America "rooming in", so that mothers may enjoy the legitimate and desirable proximity of their infants most of the time, and not be treated merely as feeding appliances.

There has recently been a recognition in most of the Children's hospitals in this country that daily visiting by the parents, and even their active help with their own children, is a good thing. One has often seen cases in Child Guidance where children of the toddler age who have been in hospital for some time without being visited have shown every type of regressive, depressive, or resentful behavior on coming home; and yet these children may have seemed to be quite happy while in hospital.[1]

The moral to be drawn from these considerations is, in the main, that we must trust Nature and follow her, as well as we are able, with our fumbling prejudiced minds. The natural laws are there, staring us in the

[1] The whole question of deprivation is dealt with in a report prepared for the World Health Organization entitled *Maternal Care and Mental Health* by Dr. John Bowlby. Also published in abbreviated form in the "Penguin" series.

face, but unperceived by us in our blindness; they apply to all that concerns man, from the ways of feeding to the organization of Society for freedom and creativity.

A lot of what we have laid down or tried to expound as being part of the mental health for which we are seeking, may have seemed obvious; we have always known the importance of maternal affection, it may be said. Maybe; but have we acted on it? Have we realized the urgency of giving it, somehow, to children deprived of it? Some of the facts given above may indicate that there is always room for rediscovery of these simple truths. Often what is instinctively known and acted upon in primitive or peasant societies, has to be rediscovered and, as it were, scientifically applied in more "civilized" ones.

What is of the greatest importance is to promote, in every way, the *natural* enjoyment of mothers in their children, not spoilt by needless anxieties and inhibitions, not hedged around with endless rules and warnings. Natural childbirth, natural feeding, relaxation and enjoyment—these things should be taught to young married people, before and after they have their children. The psychology which they need to know is neither difficult nor strange: it will point out merely what happens in the normal course of things, what to expect, how to tolerate and understand the various little (or big) difficulties which may, and usually will, arise at different ages; not to expect a degree of understanding and control in their children which is far beyond their capacity. It is astonishing sometimes what foolish parents will expect, and what punishments they may inflict for behavior which is perfectly natural.

The importance of tolerating the toddler's self-assertion and activity; of being patient, interested, and truthful in answering children's questions; of the preparation for the arrival of the next brother or sister; the acceptance of some jealousy; the meaning of discipline and habit; the origin of fears: such is the kind of information, with illustrative examples, which can be passed on. And also the comforting fact that most difficulties come in phases, and pass off naturally, if treated calmly. The danger of badly assimilated knowledge, acquired by reading or hearsay, is that it may cause anxious young parents to become still more anxious, and thus bring on the very things they fear.

The child *must* have security based on love: the wrong kind of love will spoil him, the lack of it equally may ruin him.

Let me end by quoting Fr. Keenan,[1] who puts the matter with such point:

There are fathers who care more for their geraniums, and mothers who seek consolation for their frigid husbands in their child's affection. There are jealous husbands who resent the affection given to the child. There are stupid wives who deliberately annoy their husbands by overfussing with the child. And, God forgive them, there are parents who resent the presence of the child and drag it through neurotic hell, where wave after wave of wordless misery sweep over its soul and fill it with blackness and despair in the golden age of its innocence, when it needs something of the love of the Mother of God.

[1] *Neurosis and the Sacraments* by Alan Keenan, O.F.M., Sheed & Ward, 1950, p. 68.

2

Child Guidance Treatment

Child Guidance Clinics exist for the study and treatment of maladjusted children, generally of school age. (Those for younger children are more likely to be known as Parent Guidance Clinics.) They are generally staffed by three types of specialists: a psychologist, a psychiatrist (i.e. a medically qualified specialist) and a psychiatric social worker (i.e. a social worker with extra training in psychiatric work, both with adults and children). These three constitute the child guidance "team"; reasons for this arrangement should emerge as we discuss treatment.

Now treatment depends on diagnosis, and this depends above all, not only in all medicine, but especially so in psychological disorders, on a careful and detailed history of the trouble. We have to know when the symptoms were first shown, and what were the circumstances at the time, i.e. what was going on, at home, in school, in the child. We have to know the background of the family: to get the feel of it, past and present. We have to know in detail the development of the child, his illnesses, times spent in hospital, his reactions to all the people round him and, finally, his school history, capacities, hobbies, interests.

All this is usually obtained by the social worker, amplified in other details by the psychiatrist. The psychologist gives the child intelligence tests and personality tests, to estimate the potential capacity of the child both in respect of his intelligence and of his capacity to use it. A child who lacks concentration, energy, and perseverance, cannot make full use of his intelligence, which the tests may have shown to be there. Often it is said in school reports: "This child could do better if he tried"; to which one psychiatrist made the answer: "He would try, if he were better."

The next step is to discuss the case and decide whether he should be seen by the psychiatrist (who may not be a full-time member of the "team"). It may be a case that can be dealt with by the psychologist, or social worker, or both; or it may show features which indicate that the health history and the present physical condition are important; where there seems to be a deeper disorder of the personality; or again where the mental condition of the parent is likely to have a bearing on the child. In these cases the psychiatrist should be responsible for the diagnosis. Apart from cases mainly of scholastic difficulties, which can be dealt with in the school situation, there will be few cases sufficiently disturbed to be referred to a Clinic, which do not merit the opinion of the psychiatrist, even if he, or she, only takes on a certain number for actual treatment.

We find that the symptoms or complaints for which children are referred fall into two main groups: firstly, the behavior problems, such as violent tempers, defiance, truancy, stealing; secondly, the nervous conditions, such as fears, timidity, and "habit disorders" such as disturbed sleep, incontinence, twitching, and so on. We know also that usually there is a combination of these. Even the apparently aggressive child will be insecure and guilty underneath, and the neurotic child will bring out his repressed aggression in the course of treatment. Often enough a child will be referred for one symptom, and will be found to have others even more important. Treatment therefore is not so much based on the symptoms, as on the degree and depth of the general disturbance in the child's personality, and on the different causes or factors behind it. Now these causes are both in the child and in his environment; they are in the past and in the present; they are social, intellectual, and emotional; hence the type of treatment will be directed according to where the main stresses are to be found, while the rôle of the different members of the team will vary accordingly.

Let us take first the rôle of the psychologist. In addition to the tests which he (or she) carries out, to establish the intellectual capacity of the child, he investigates any special difficulties with school subjects, and visits the school to discuss progress and behavior with the child's teachers. He may then decide that remedial teaching—which is more than just "coaching"

—is indicated at the Clinic. Often the difficulty with learning lies more in the emotional sphere: the child is too discouraged or anxious to use his capacity, so the educational side in the narrower sense cannot be isolated from the whole problem. The psychologist may also carry out therapy with the child, according to aptitude and training.

The work of the psychiatric social worker is, as the title indicates, both social and psychiatric: social in so far as she is concerned with the material conditions under which the child lives, giving advice and help where this is needed, paying visits to the home in some cases. The psychiatric side of her work consists in interviews with the parent week by week, this being itself a therapeutic process, in the course of which the mother, and/or father, discuss their problems, difficulties in married life, management of their children, and so on. In the course of this process, they come to understand their own attitudes, perhaps in the light of their own childhood, and in this way become more tolerant and more hopeful. This is done by listening with understanding rather than by any didactic attitude; there is no question of blame or censure, which would merely arouse more guilt and resentment; one has to understand and to forgive—which may not be easy!

EXAMPLES

At this point it would be well to illustrate some of these rather theoretical points by an actual example.

A boy of ten was referred by the Principal because he was falling very much behind in his work at school. It is found that he is moody, unsociable, and quarrelsome at home, that he takes long to go to sleep, and that he has many fears relating to his health: he is afraid of his heart, he thinks he may die. For the latter reason he is afraid to go to school, but he continues to make brave efforts to do so, though obviously ill with anxiety every morning. He is first seen by the psychologist, who finds that the boy is much too disturbed to do any tests. He is, in fact, in an almost psychotic state of anxiety, depression, and confusion. He is the second of three children, with a much older and a much younger brother. He has a good home and good parents. There has been a good deal of illness in the family, and about the time that the boy's symptoms started, the big brother had been killed in the East. The mother had become apathetic, and was moreover expecting to go to the hospital for an operation, which she did during the course of treatment of the boy. Apart from some earlier events in the boy's lifestory, these were the main features.

He attended weekly for treatment by the psychiatrist for several months, and made slow improvement. At school he was treated with the utmost consideration, as the psychologist testified. The mother attended as well, and, while co-operative, could not bring herself to respond or to open up much. She was changed to an older and more experienced social worker and became easier and more relaxed; she then divulged that her son out East had married a native girl by whom there was a child, and she had known nothing of this until she received photos after his death. She has come to accept this strange and romantic relationship, which is no longer a shameful family secret.

There is little doubt that the boy was affected by his mother's troubles, and, was, as we would say, "identified" closely with her. His improvement has coincided with her own. He has begun to lose his fears, and to become more sociable; he attends school regularly. His own treatment has consisted of reassurance, explanation of bodily processes (which are matters of concern and anxiety to disturbed children) and a certain amount of self-expression with sand-tray apparatus and painting. Recently he described a dream in which he saw another boy lying wounded, and also a black man dead. It may not be too far fetched to see in these two figures his other selves: it is another part of himself who is wounded; the black man may stand for his "shadow-self" which is laid to rest.

We see, in this case, a long process of drawing-out or unravelling of a complex situation; a process of collaboration between social worker and psychiatrist. It also illustrates a distinctive feature of Child Guidance, namely treatment conducted at a level deeper than mere surface adjustments in the home or school; one which involves unconscious elements, hence a process which is analytic, and derives from the knowledge provided by depth psychology, as well as the "common-sense" approach (which some people seem to think is all that is necessary in Child Guidance).

Let me add too that the case is not finished. Difficulties may lie ahead, for example at puberty. Sometimes difficulties recur, in a different form, perhaps years later. It is often easy enough to effect an apparent "cure", and to have the same case cropping up later. I have followed enough cases now at intervals until adulthood to realize this, and also to be encouraged by the fact that even slight help and support given at critical moments later, for example at adolescence, may help them to win through without a real breakdown.

VARIETIES OF TREATMENT

There is obviously a great variety in the type of treatment applied to different cases; in some, perhaps a third of the cases, a full diagnosis, with some advice and general clarification, may be all that is required. In about another third of the total, changes in the management of the child, and a short process of treatment, will serve to clear up the situation. In the remainder, who show more serious and difficult problems of neurosis and behavior, psychotherapy of the child is the heart of the matter.

This, if anything, is the most important aspect of Child Guidance; the discovery of the inner world of the child's mind, and the means of unlocking it by special techniques, is perhaps the most revolutionary and far-reaching development in the field of mental health.

It is based, whatever its variations, and the apparently opposed theories of psychologists and psychiatrists, on the researches of Freud into the deeper layers of the human mind. Whatever variety of techniques may be used, child therapy has certain elements about which there is general agreement among Child Guidance workers in all countries. These may be described as follows: the provision of a situation which will enable the child to give free expression to his instinctive and emotional life, i.e. his loves and hates (ambivalent feelings), his fears and desires, his curiosity or guilt about the instinctive functions: nutrition, excretion, reproduction. In this situation there is established a certain relationship between child and therapist, which again is unique, and in which the therapist acts as a kind of bridge between the world of the child and that of adults, between fantasy and reality, between danger and security. The child communicates with the therapist, and also with himself, by means of a language which is not merely expressed in words (and often very little in words) but chiefly through play.

One of the favorite instruments in the technique of "play-therapy" is a shallow box with sand, wet or dry, which can be used to produce a scene, or "world".[1] This is done by means of the rich material, provided in the shops, of lead figures: animals, soldiers, cowboys (which can be obtained in such profuse variety and of such excellent workmanship), not to mention houses, trees, fences, and cars. These scenes vary greatly, though they tend to be either peaceful

[1] This term was originated by Dr. Margaret Lowenfeld who was the first to describe this particular piece of apparatus.

farm scenes, or battles; redskin *v.* cowboy being a favorite theme.

The meek, quiet child can thus express his suppressed aggression, or the turbulent, insecure one his desire for peace and quiet! In a series of such scenes, week by week, we are shown as it were a panorama of the child's mind—both conscious and unconscious. Children can become quite absorbed in a fantasy of make-belief in this way, and the very act of expressing their conflicts and desires in this vivid and concrete manner, seems to have a curative effect. This is enhanced if some interpretation of the inner or unconscious meaning of the scene is given to the child (a technique which requires sound analytical knowledge, tact and skill, and one not to be lightly undertaken). Painting and modelling are also used in various ways. Small children have usually little hesitation in putting brush to paper, but older children often need a good deal of encouragement before they will attempt it. Pictures again can be very revealing of a child's personality, and also afford a means of self-expression and emotional satisfaction. Play-therapy is done either individually or in small groups, the object and method being different in each case.

Through this medium of the imagination, the child as it were comes to terms with his emotions, which are largely unconscious to him. He comes to realize the connection between his symptoms and those feelings which have disturbed him; to accept these as less dangerous and terrible than he had imagined them—as being in a sense natural—and thus to be freed from the hold which they had upon him. He is also encouraged in his interests, and helped to realize his good characteristics and possibilities.

Play is also diagnostic, because it shows the stage in emotional development of the child, and the extent to which he tends to regress to earlier interests and behavior. The Unconscious is said to be timeless, so it contains material from infancy onwards, which is still active, still causing the child to behave in some respects as though he were at a much earlier stage of growth. Traumatic events, rejections, jealousies, deprivations, punishment or threats from the past, keep him back, or haunt him in the present; so to understand the genesis and the nature of the disturbances which we are trying to cure, we must know something about the natural or normal development of the instinctive-emotional life, to which we turn in the next section.

3

Natural Development

Nothing is more certain in the study of mental and neurotic disorders, as well as in character disorders such as delinquency, than the origin of these in terms of *relationships* between the child and his parents, brothers, sisters, and later, other people. It is also certain that what happens within these relationships from early infancy, is of vital importance in the formation of the personality, and its deviations.

Now, what does happen in early infancy is mainly feeding, sleeping and excreting; then successively an urge to self-assertion, a desire to explore and experiment, and the recognition of other people. From quite early on there is of course an interchange of sympathy, expressed in affection and fun, between mother and child. But an important point is that these relationships are expressed largely through the physical functions; it is not therefore just a matter of sucking, eating, excreting, washing, and so on, but of how these important matters are carried out.

Too much frustration, too much rigidity, too much tension or irritation on the part of the mother, a lack of tolerance and warmth—all these early happenings, which might seem trivial, or soon forgotten, are now known to be vital links in the formation of the personality. Affection, security, and satisfaction are just as vital to the child's emotional growth as are calories and vitamins in the physical.

The first of these functions then is feeding, the so-called "oral" stage. At the beginning of things the infant horizon is bounded by the breast, or its substitute, and the physical and sensual satisfaction of this need is the be-all of existence. We have fortunately come to realize that what is natural is best, and that feeding strictly by the clock, with elaborate formulae, is not as desirable from any point of view as used to be thought until recently. We even tend to agree that more digestive troubles are caused by not feeding enough to the child than by the opposite, that in fact the child in his nature is our real guide. Children at the breast vary a great deal in their habits; some are lazy feeders, but it can hardly be a good thing for nurses to slap, prod and push these babies to hurry them up, and make the mother anxious.

The next stage is that of excretion, and this again is not just a physical function, but seems to have important psychological bearings. It is after all the first thing that the child feels that he can give or withhold. He becomes aware that the way he performs this "duty" is a source of satisfaction or of displeasure to the parent. This should be obvious from the fact that failure of control later (in the form of enuresis and still more encopresis) may be a symptom of failure in emotional development, regression to childish behavior, or a sign of resentment, even when there are physical conditions involved as well; also that too early an insistence on cleanliness, too much fussing about constipation and so on, may well produce a breakdown of this control.

Later on, together with the increasing independence and self-assertion of the toddler, we may note the interest in sex, exploration of the genitals, and so on, which is discussed in a later chapter. At this age we find infantile fantasies about birth. Tolerance and freedom at this stage are most important, especially if life is being made more difficult by the arrival of a brother or sister; otherwise we find anxiety and guilt resulting outwardly in aggressive behavior, which if not recognized as denoting insecurity, and if treated merely by punishment, makes matters worse.

RELATIONSHIPS

The relationship of the child towards his father and mother is also being established, and is perhaps the most crucial stage of all. It is held that the small boy tends to an exclusive possessiveness of his mother, with jealousy towards the father, whom he comes to admire however, and then acquires a satisfactory relation to both. The opposite, with some modification, occurs in the case of the girl. This is the famous Oedipus complex. This process occurs mainly unconsciously, and is therefore not obvious to those who question the child or parent and then deny its existence as a Freudian fantasy. In maladjusted or disturbed children however it is often obvious enough, even to an outspoken declaration of wishing to take the place of the rival parent in bed!

I have treated cases where symptoms of insomnia, phobias, tempers, etc., have started when the child has been ousted from sleeping in the parents' room, or where the father has returned home after some long absence in war, and the boy has been alone with his mother: jealousy in such cases is far from being merely at an unconscious level. This situation may be activated at adolescence, and it is unfortunately too evident that the fixation of the boy emotionally on his mother can cause a deviation of the erotic life on to a homosexual level.

It is not necessary however to regard this threefold relationship in terms of "incestuous" attachments, for it is wider and deeper than that. It is a process of growth and development where father, mother and child must play their respective rôles. The father must be neither tyrant nor weak; the mother must be womanly—both wife and mother—if the child is not to feel either rejected and resentful, or held back and dependent.

The process of forming a satisfactory relationship— of resolving the conflicts in the triangular contest, so to speak—seems to be most active between the ages of two to five: the toddler and infant stage. After this there comes a more gregarious phase, when children are less concerned with their parents than with each other; they are less individual and more of a group, wanting to be like others, eager for games and gang activities. Later we come to the phase of pre-puberty and early adolescence, where once again children tend to become more individual, more conscious of a separate self and therefore at times moody and difficult.

PHASES

In all their different ages there may be times when children become "difficult", moody, or nervous. Parents do not need to suppose that because of this their children are becoming "maladjusted", or that they need rush them off to the nearest psychiatrist. There are many phases that are lived through and pass away. Patience, humor and tolerance are the best treatment. It is only when these phases are very prolonged and are making the child ill, miserable, and unable to work at school, or play and mix with others, that we need such expert advice.

Children grow and develop through a process of inner unfolding, not by being molded as though they were inert and passive material—a kind of wax tablet on which we adults are to imprint a set of rules. Neither is the effect of the environment as a whole a direct and simple one. Each child reacts as a distinct individual; the relationship is a double one. It is obvious for example how two children from the same family will react quite differently. Moreover, not only is the child influenced by this relationship to its family circle, but the parents in turn are influenced in their reactions, and even in their characters, by their children.

The effects therefore are not merely superficial ones, found in conformity of behavior, or obedience to rules, but there are also effects at a deeper level. These may include feelings of guilt and frustration, conflicts between the desire to grow up to independence on the one hand, and yet to retain security and approval on the other.

Physical symptoms, moods, fears, or tempers are to be seen in the light of these deeper tensions and relationships which are, in fact, "unconscious".

Realizing these matters does not mean that we, as parents, are to be even more concerned as to our fitness or otherwise to bring up children: given that we provide them with the right kind of emotional climate —as far from worry and fuss, as "relaxed" as possible— our proper task is to watch them with loving observation, and learn from them what they need for their unfolding. It is by enjoying them in this way that we promote their mental welfare, not by reading books about psychology and becoming anxious!

SENSITIVE PERIODS

We must not forget that the growing infant or child is not merely a creature of instincts and emotions, but also a sentient, intelligent being, whose development depends not only on relationships with people but on a group of things, activities, processes; in short on a relation to the whole environment.

Montessori, whose observations on childhood were so revealing (going beyond her educational methods), has discovered some of these secrets of development for us.

One of her main observations, drawn from the field of biology, was what she called the "Sensitive Periods". This means that at certain definite moments in a child's life there is a readiness for certain types of knowledge and activity, which has to be watched for and satisfied. Psychological development does not come by chance, nor does it originate merely in stimuli from the outer world; it is guided by transient sensibilities, temporary instincts, as it were, for the acquisition of different characteristics. "The inner sensibilities . . . determine the section of necessary things from a diverse environment, and of circumstances favorable to development. . . . In these sense relations between the child and his environment, lies the key to the mysterious recess in which the spiritual embryo achieves the miracles of growth". "When something hinders its inner working, the existence of the sensitive period shows itself by violent reactions: a despair that we believe to be causeless, and therefore put down to naughtiness and temper." [1]

One example of a similar period is the necessity which children feel for *order*: for things to be, and things to happen, in a rightful place and in a rightful manner. A baby placed in a strange bed, a small child

[1] In *The Secret of Childhood*, Longmans, 1936.

finding things in the wrong place, may be considerably upset. Perhaps it is this sense of order—of things being right, of normal repetition—which is frustrated when children are not all the time with one person, handled in the same way, and have to adjust to different handling all the time.

There is another sensitivity which develops early; this is the inner feeling which gives him a sense of the different parts of his body, their movement and position in space: his inner orientation. The child has a highly developed sensitivity in respect of the positions of his body, long before he can move freely and make experiments. These observations are in line with the importance nowadays attributed to what is known as the "body-image" or schema. It seems that if this inner as well as outer "orientation" of the child is not fostered by sufficient handling and caressing by adults during infancy, there may result a lack of contact with reality and a lack of relationship to others, which may end in a form of schizophrenia.

At about the age of two, interest in large objects and bright color seems to wane, and an interest in minute detail takes its place: another example of the observation of a new sensitive period. Montessori likens this inner guide, which leads children to that which the spirit requires for its unfolding, to Dante's "intelligence of love".

A very great change has indeed occurred in the understanding of the child mind in our day. It used to be supposed, and still may be by those with minds sufficiently out of date, that the child is a kind of empty vessel to be filled by an adult—who of course knows what is good for the child.

We have now to regard the function of the adult as one which must lovingly *observe* and learn a child's needs, and provide the environment necessary for the unfolding from within. He must accept the fact that the child instinctively, or intuitively, knows what is necessary and what is best for his development—if he can discover it. This is not a process of "giving in" to the child, but of allowing him to fulfill his natural development. By this means he achieves stability, order, happiness, and indeed goodness, through an inner discipline without the panoply of reward or punishment, the urging, coaxing and scolding which we tend to think necessary to train the "stubborn, wilful, ignorant" nature of children. Without a knowledge of these "laws": "the adult and the child, made to love one another, find themselves in conflict through an incomprehension that corrodes the roots of life, and which takes place in impenetrable secrecy."

There are of course many more aspects of normal child development which cannot be mentioned in a short chapter. I have only touched the fringe of the subject. I have hardly mentioned the vast subject of intelligence and learning, because it is beyond the scope of a short book.

4

Sex In Childhood

"Let me praise thee, O Lord, for my Brother Body, for
thou hast created him to be the most beautiful of all
visible things!"—St. Francis.

The idea that there is in childhood, even in the earliest years before the age of five, a considerable amount
of interest and activity which can be described as
sexual, is one that seems startling and incredible. It is
not of course sexual in the full sense because the organs and glands of sex are not mature, but it is a fact
that the interest and the "experimentation," as one
may put it, of young children in bodily differences,
their capacity for stimulating erotic sensation, have a
particular intensity and quality about them which
renders them at least akin to sex. Those who maintain
that these activities are no different to any other form
of curiosity or pleasure in physical activity in childhood, are unaware of, or refuse to accept the evidence
for, their essential difference.

This early "embryonic" sex life is obscure and
largely unconscious; the degree to which it may be

manifest varies a great deal with temperament, and with the child's experience with other more precocious children. Normally it goes partially underground at about the age of six, with the onset of a more social or "gang" phase, and again becomes more active at puberty, or just before it. In children who are disturbed in their emotional development owing to a bad environment, the sexual instincts are less controlled and harmonized, and may become manifest at any age. It is important therefore not to isolate sex difficulties and behavior from the rest of the child's personality, but to realize that they are often means of seeking the attention and friendship which he has lacked. It is a way of filling an emotional vacuum, and is found to go with other forms of aggressive, unstable, and delinquent behavior.

Again, many of these emotionally disturbed children have witnessed or heard of uncontrolled adult sexual life, or have been "interfered" with, so that sex for them acquires an almost obsessional quality, highly charged with emotion. To carry out a detailed inquisition on sex misconduct (as is sometimes done by the police) is bad for all concerned; it is the child's whole personality which needs to be considered and treated.

Any sexual form of behavior at any age, but especially in the younger children (here I am speaking of normal children as well) must not be met with signs of disgust and horror, because this is the surest way to fix it in the child's mind, with the result that he may be prevented from ever acquiring a normal healthy attitude to sex in the future.

What is certain in the experience of every psychiatrist is that undue severity in these matters, inducing a feeling of excessive guilt, may have most serious consequences later. I have seen more than one case where these early "perversions" were unwisely handled with the result that later, usually at adolescence, there was a regression to similar behavior which then became truly a perversion; or other cases where one of the roots of severe neurosis was the punishment meted out in childhood for some incident of this sort.

SEX ENLIGHTENMENT

We have become aware therefore of two aspects of sex in childhood; one being the realization that sex is no longer considered to appear fully developed only at adolescence, but that it does manifest itself, if only in shadowy and primitive forms, and in various stages, from early childhood; though it may not be consciously realized as such till adolescence. Secondly, it is not to be considered as an isolated aspect of the self, but as an integral part of the personality; so that it not only permeates, as it were, the whole self, but also develops, is expressed, and experienced according to the nature and development of that personality. This is shown by the fact that the more maladjusted or neurotic the child, the more is there likely to be some form of abnormal or at least exaggerated sex behavior.

These two aspects have a bearing on the subject of sex education: a vexed subject with which we now have to come to grips. In the first place it is clear that it has to begin very young, and there is really no great difficulty about this, at least in theory, since it is agreed that the questions of a small child on the subject should be answered simply, but frankly and truthfully. Secondly, it follows that a mere knowledge of the physical aspects of sex is not enough to avoid trouble and to promote a normal healthy attitude towards it. (Freud himself points out that mere sex instruction might do more harm than anything; in this, as in other things, he is much maligned!) It is a subject of knowledge which has to be integrated as a *human* function with the social, moral, and spiritual aspects of the human person. Moreover, it is highly charged with emotions of all kinds: wonder, curiosity, desire, guilt. It ranges from animal lust to the most exalted forms of love. "Everything is received according to the mode of the receiver" and a knowledge of sex may be accepted by one child with calmness, another with awe, another as a joke, yet another as an incitement to direct action! This is an argument against the giving of class instruction on human sex, since it must be given to a large group of a heterogeneous kind, with very different temperaments, attitudes, and morals.

To return to the beginning: the ideal way of sex education, in the full context of education, comes by way of the parents' replies to their children's questions at all ages. We are met with the difficulty however that children vary, even in the same family, as to the extent of their questions; some will ask lots and some never a one. If the parents have suffered from much "repression" themselves, the children are dimly aware that any question will cause embarrassment. Many parents, even of a younger generation, are unable to answer these questions sensibly. Recently a mother told me how her small boy aged six, on the occasion of the arrival of a new baby, asked at table where it came from. The granny said "Don't be rude"; the mother tried to correct this unfortunate impression by saying that it came from under her apron. No doubt the young man would then associate this with something from under the counter!

The enlightenment of older children is not an easy matter because it is difficult to know how much they already know, and how much it is advisable for them to be told at a particular age. It depends obviously on the kind of environment from which they come, i.e. whether they have led a sheltered kind of life or whether they are likely to have picked up bits and pieces. But most of them nowadays probably know more than one thinks.

They may have learned biology at school, carried up to the reproductive process in mammals; this is however but a preliminary, and a very different matter to the integral knowledge of sex in the human, which has obviously far wider implications. It has to include the social, emotional and moral aspects. It has a personal application for each one. For example, from the beginning the difference in bodily formation between the sexes may have aroused curiosity and some concern. Little girls have been known to weep because they thought they had lost something which their brothers had and they did not; or they may think that it has been cut off. Little boys may have been stupidly threatened with having their organs cut off if they played with them. This is known as castration fear, and it may cause real mental disturbance.

Later on, at puberty, they will have to learn that there are sensations and events which are normal: menstruation in the case of girls, erection and emission in the case of boys; that these are the beginnings of the power to produce new life, which must be guarded and respected in virtue of what they mean in adult life.

It can never be a simple matter to educate any child or adolescent in human sex. How can it be, when it ranges from the heights of romance and sublimity to the depths of lust and perversion? Yet it must not be made too mysterious and too awesome: it is also something familiar, tender, even playful. It is small wonder that one hesitates to propound rules or provide any easy solution. The way in which sex will be met and accepted depends on so many things: on early emotional development, on the family environment, on temperament and intelligence, and so on. Yet it remains true, I think, that the simple physical facts must be taught in appropriate stages, and then fitted into the context of life as a whole: life as it ought to be.

There is no doubt that we are not tackling the problem with honesty and consistency, and that it must be done. In certain schools run by nuns there is a scheme of sex education which seems quite admirable, and deserves recognition and adoption. It is this: short pamphlets are written, suitable to different ages, which can either be read by the mother to the girl, or by the girl herself, or both separately. The question of how they are to be used is discussed first with the teacher, who propounds the idea to the parent. In this way the parents' right and duty in the matter are safeguarded, the instruction can be given frankly, fully, and in the right words, and the teacher is brought into it as well. There is complete elasticity as to choice of method according to the temperament, age, and feeling of each participant.

In this way the whole subject of sex and morality can be put in the right perspective at those ages—pre-puberty and adolescence—when these matters have to be assimilated and integrated within a new awareness, no matter what the child may already know. In this way the ideas of modesty and chastity which are integral to Christian and Catholic belief can be understood and practised—not as negative virtues proceeding from prudery and fear of sex, but as something positive, belonging to the high dignity and value which sex should have.

5

Delinquency

"In this life there is no punishment for punishment's sake. . . . The value of human penalties is medicinal and in so far as they promote public security or the cure of the criminal."—St. Thomas Aquinas, *Summa*.

CAUSATION

Delinquency means an offence against the law. There are many kinds of offence and many different types of delinquents. Some are normal boys up to mischief; some may be potential criminals. The great majority of delinquents are boys and the commonest type of offence is theft. The girls are more likely to be out of control, or involved in immoral conduct. These are facts; but when we come to the causes of delinquency and its treatment, we find innumerable views and theories. Indeed one may say that delinquency has become a touchstone whereby you can judge a person's temperament, beliefs, and even class. At one extreme you have the man who says that delinquents are just naughty boys who deserve a sharp lesson, preferably by means of corporal punishment. At the other ex-

treme is the psychiatrist or psychologist who affirms
that we know very little about the subject, and that a
vast amount of research, accompanied by elaborate
statistics, is required.

The first type is inclined to consider as sentimental-
ists those who talk of psychological causes and treatment, but it is they who are such, because their views
are based precisely on some presupposition or preju-
dice. It is the experts in the subject who are realists
because they study the matter objectively from every
angle, in order to arrive at a fairly exact appraisal of
each case, and to give a considered opinion as to the
best method by which delinquents may be made more
or less useful members of society.

I would maintain that by now we know quite a lot
about delinquency. The first thing that might be said
is that the great majority of real delinquents are unhappy children. "Crime and happiness are like oil and
water: they don't mix." This was said by Fr. Flanagan
of Boys' Town; and he ought to know.

Why are these children unhappy? Mainly of course
because they come from unhappy homes. Now when I
say delinquents I am not thinking of the normal
naughty boys who break the law for fun, but of the
type of boys and girls who are found in Detention
Homes and Approved Schools. A recent booklet entitled *Approved School Boys* gives a very clear picture
of these boys and their background. Out of one hun-
dred taken at random, only thirty-five came from what
appeared to be normal homes; this did not mean that
the "normal" homes were necessarily emotionally or

even economically satisfactory, the report states, but only that they were not grossly bad like the others. These others included conditions such as: separation, divorce or desertion by parents; neglect, rejection, destitution and squalor. Another aspect which was much stressed was the very marked scholastic retardation of these boys. Delinquents tend to be below the average in intelligence, they are very ignorant, and they are backward in the three Rs.

Another aspect which must be considered is that of temperament, by which one means the inborn, constitutional, inherited factors in the personality. This shows itself mainly as a disturbance in growth, not only physical development but intellectual and emotional. Think for example of a physically over-developed boy or girl, with the mentality of a child. Or again of a boy with good intelligence but with delayed growth, and infantile as regards sex development, with emotional immaturity in addition. Such conditions in themselves are liable to lead to trouble. We now also recognize a type of immaturity in the brain which is shown by measuring the electric rhythms, and is found in many of the unstable types. Behavior in these cases is thus to some extent dependent on a poor control from the higher centers of the brain, causing instability and impulsive or violent actions.

Temperament then is something given, but what is made of it depends on the influences that work upon it. A boy of unstable temperament may come from a home where the parent or parents are themselves of an

inferior type and thus his bad features may be accentu-
ated. He may need to be away from home, so that he
may be helped to overcome what is weak in his personality and encourage what is potentially good. The
making of a delinquent, or of a neurotic for that
matter, is then a question of the interplay between
temperament and environment. There are those who
are born with sufficient endowment to withstand the
worst kind of upbringing, and others who succumb
easily in what appears to be a good home.

Some delinquents come from homes which appear
to be relatively happy and stable; one child alone in
such a family may turn to delinquency. Why is this?
Because that home is in some way unhappy for him
alone. He may be, or feel, the least wanted, the least
loved of the family; he may be less clever, less popu-
lar than the others.

Another factor which appears to be important in
causing delinquent behavior is that of separation
from the home for long periods. Absence from the
mother in early childhood, for example through a long
stay in a hospital, or an actual change of home, e.g. by
desertion of the mother, seems to result in a type of
character which has been described as "affectionless."
In these children, the absence at a crucial period of
emotional life, of the very prototype of human affection and happy relationship, produces a character
which is lacking in the ordinary power of response
to other individuals; there is therefore an apparent
absence of moral sense, trust, and obligation. Delin-

quents of this type are very hard, almost impossible in cases, to reform.

Whatever the conditions which disturb the even development and happiness of a child, they breed certain states of mind such as resentment, inferiority, a craving for excitement, for release from misery, frustration or mere boredom. Sooner or later these varied feelings lead to delinquent acts and their repetition—often with a kind of compulsive quality. The earlier it starts and the more the delinquent habit has been brought about by the more serious emotional factors mentioned above, the harder it is to cure, as a general rule. There are other cases which manifest their disorder only at puberty or later.

There are many cases of stealing brought to the notice of Child Guidance Clinics which are quite obviously motivated by unconscious feelings of resentment, dependency or even anxiety.

Jimmy, aged eleven, comes from a large, reasonably happy working-class family. He attends a Catholic school which he likes. He started taking money from home two years or so ago. This coincided with the mother's absence in hospital to have a baby. Then later she went into hospital seriously ill and the family were told that she might die. As soon as she got over this, Jimmy started to steal again, in a kind of burst of relief, after his anxiety. There was no other possible motive, and the association of the two was clear. His realization of this helped him to overcome this tendency.

Robert, aged thirteen, a Grammar School boy, has

been stealing for a long time. Not only this but he is unsocial and lethargic, he is falling behind in his work although intelligent enough according to his I.Q. The trouble appears to have started when his father who is a policeman came back from the Army and started to lay down the law; he is obviously still too restrictive. So we get a dreary tale of punishment, transgression, discouragement. The school was also inclined to impose constant penalties in the vain hope of mending his ways. With the help of the Child Guidance team, the atmosphere changed gradually on all sides, the boy no longer steals, and is doing better in school.

The above are success stories, and there are many cases where these gentle methods fail—perhaps through lack of skill in applying them. They are meant to illustrate the fact that many "delinquents" are in fact maladjusted children who have come up against the law.

TREATMENT

It may seem by now to the reader that amid this welter of causes, factors, and conditioning there is left no room for moral responsibility or the realization that delinquency is in fact the breaking of the Law, and usually a transgression of the moral code as well. Whether this is so or not, depends in the final issue on a religious or philosophical belief. Given all the possible conditioning factors, we may say that these determined the action: that the child could do no other. Or we may say that no matter what the provocation and incitement, there is always at bottom the possibility of control, of choice, therefore of responsibility. From the latter follows the idea of restitution to be made, which may include punishment, such as loss of liberty.

The idea of absolute responsibility, even for a child, and the savage penalties which followed even minor theft, held sway in the past century and showed the degrading depths to which so-called righteous people can descend in cruelty; all in the name of justice and morality. Even now many "good" people will maintain that it all boils down to wrong-doing which must be punished, no matter how many facts about a particular case may be brought forward. The truth of the matter is that each case is different. They range from those children who are defective or who have had some disease of the brain, down to those who are normal enough in themselves, and come from normal circumstances, so that they can be considered fully responsible.

It should however be clear by now that to advocate repressive discipline as a means of curing the majority of real delinquents is not only unjust but stupid. It is like saying that those who are badly nourished should have less food. Most of these children have been deprived of human affection and of understanding; they need more of it, not less.

Fortunately we can claim that more enlightened ideas and methods are increasingly spreading in most parts of the world. It should not be forgotten that the human and Christian way of rescuing delinquent youth was started at the beginning of last century in Milan by St. John Bosco, and the lessons which he taught have been applied since then in schools run by the Order which he founded: the Salesians. The nature of his ideas can be seen in the following extracts from his life by Henri Ghéon:

> He saw before him the mind of a child; he refused to constrain it. A school for him was the very antithesis of a barracks or a prison. It was a place of election, windswept, living, where souls and bodies grow together for their flowering.

Again:

> There must be a minimum of "discipline" in the class-room; complete liberty outside it. This liberty is not so much supervised by the master, as observed, directed, and gradually shaped. The master must know each boy, take an interest in all that interests boys—his family, work, tastes and pleasures—as much as would a friend of his own age and even more.
>
> If a boy has behaved badly, he must be punished only in the last resort, and without humiliation or violence; if possible the worst of the punishment should be his master's sorrow.

One can only wish that his precepts were known and acted upon by all those who run schools of a reformatory type for the young. There are a number of schools of the Boys' Town type in Italy, mostly run under the direction of some enlightened priest, of which the Boys' Republic at Civita Vecchia is perhaps the best known. An interesting feature here is that the boys are split up into sections according to their bent, for farming, the sea, or industrial and craft work. They run a good deal of their affairs themselves by means of their "parliament", thus learning democratic practice in the most telling way. All over Europe and America such places can be found, serving as a model and gradually altering the régime of old-fashioned, rigid, and repressive institutions, which unfortunately still exist in large numbers.

To visit institutions which are inspired by imagination and kindness is to find oases of hope in a world parched by the hate and waste of war.

There are still, no doubt, in many places, schools of the reforming type, where a system prevails of rigid discipline combined with concentrated doses of religion. In such places it is certain that boys' characters are "toughened": that they learn how to evade authority and how to escape punishment; also that they will discard the religion which they have been taught by those whom they may fear but do not love. Even in the better forms of Approved Schools there tends to be too much "order": everything is cut and dried, and boys cannot learn responsibility, initiative, and self-discipline. They should be prepared for the life they will find outside—not regulated into an unreal existence. There has been however a definite improvement in the whole spirit and method of "reform"; here at least we can say that there has been progress.

6

Residential Treatment of Maladjusted Children

Of children who can be considered to be maladjusted, probably about one in ten will require to be sent away from home. It is not merely a separation from home which is required, but a special form of treatment which it is the purpose of this chapter to describe.

Such children are those who have proved refractory to other methods of handling, at home or at school; or those whose homes are too bad, from the emotional rather than the material aspect. The decision to remove them from home will have been made after a period of observation—brief or prolonged—at a Child Guidance Clinic. It is in fact part of treatment.

The types of cases which require to be sent to special residential schools are best described by actual examples:

Bobby, aged seven, is the second child of a Protestant mother and a Catholic Irish father. The mother got T.B. during her third pregnancy and was in a sanatorium for two years, leaving three children with the grandmother. The mother came home and a fourth, then a fifth child were born. Mother again got T.B. and the children were placed in a Children's Home. Bobby began to pilfer, swear, and was at the same time pathetically dependent on a young teacher. He developed violent cruelty to animals. He was fostered with a kindly woman who, however, was unable to keep him.

The child is not psychotic or defective: he has merely turned against everything and everybody because he has been so grievously hurt. He is the product of feckless, foolish parents, who yet are affectionate, and the child has felt abandoned.

Charlie, aged nine, of good intelligence. Referred because of violent tempers and bullying. The father is epileptic and has violent rages. Divorce proceedings are pending. Meanwhile the mother is doing her best for six children. Charlie shows tremendous repressed aggression in his play but is friendly, artistic and probably good material if in the right environment.

Children sent to schools for the maladjusted are not in the main those who come from homes which are hopeless from either a material or moral point of view; such children are best taken into care by the Children's Officer and found some more permanent home. (Deprived children are not necessarily maladjusted in any case, but suffering from the effects of bad environment, i.e. they are not mentally sick children.) The home, bad or rejecting though it may be, must offer some hope of co-operation, some basis upon which to build a better future for the child.

Some of the children indeed come from homes which are apparently normal enough but where there have occurred such severe psychological clashes and conflicts that the situation, between parents and child, has become impossible. Although I could describe some tragic and pathetic cases of rejection, I prefer to select a case from the home of respectable and well-meaning parents:

Jane, aged nine, was a very stormy child. She was impossibly aggressive at school, and beyond her parents' control at home. Her mother was a weak, well-meaning person, dominated by a harsh and rigid husband. It was not a case of spare the rod, because the father in fact used too much of it on the girl—on principle—and only made her more defiant. It was obviously an emotional tangle between the three. It was such a profound and violent one that it could not be unravelled by Clinic treatment (psychotherapy) alone. Her behavior at the Clinic was violent, and the male parental attitude was quite intransigent. She was sent to a school for maladjusted children where I have watched her progress for two or three years. She continued a stormy career, being wild, noisy and even violent. But she had charm, a capacity for dancing, and her moments of tenderness, especially towards her rabbits. With the approach of puberty, she softened further, as many hard cases will, and she learned to make attachments to people who understood and tolerated her. Now she is back at home and at a normal school, and her father has even admitted that his methods might have been wrong.

There are however cases of children with no homes, or with hopelessly broken-up homes, who have to be sent to schools for the maladjusted because there is nothing else for them; and they must be given a chance. These cases may require a long term of treatment, until well into adolescence: a fact not always realized by the authorities concerned.

The following is a case in point:

A girl of ten, illegitimate, was taken in to a Convent Home at the age of two. She became more and more difficult as she grew older, being very aggressive with other children, stealing, also enuretic and soiling.

By the time she was seven, she had become a positive danger, and had to be excluded from school, and removed from the Home. Wisely, she was sent first to a hospital, where she was observed, tested, and treated. She was found to be physically normal, of intelligence below average; she showed marked lack of understanding which was considered to be emotionally caused. At first in the hospital she was over active and aggressive, but as she formed fruitful relationships with the staff, she became relaxed and friendly, the soiling stopped, she began to read. She is still however a difficult and disturbed child; she would break down for certain in a more rigid environment, and will need several years in the residential school for maladjusted children where she has been sent, in order to acquire the stability and social sense which she needs.

Here then was a "deprived child", who was treated with a combination of ordinary care, punishment, and religion, without any effect, except that she got worse and worse. It was not realized that she was a sick child in the sense that she needed to start all over again, and be treated with affection and toleration as though she were an infant, until she could begin to feel accepted and wanted. She may already have had some basis of security before she was two, which was abruptly broken off. This destroyed her chance of acquiring a moral sense or capacity for normal relationships; her whole being was developing in a state of disintegration, and needed a very special environment if she was to develop at all normally. A child in this state may be too late to achieve normality; in this case fortunately, there are signs that she will recover.

In estimating the personalities of these children, and the extent to which we can alter and improve them, it is obvious that heredity has to be allowed for. The degree of intelligence itself is largely an inherited factor, as is also the temperament. In some of these very difficult children especially, there is a considerable element of constitutional (that is, inborn) instability. Sometimes this takes the form of an epileptic tendency, which can actually be demonstrated by measuring the electric waves or rhythms in the brain. This may run in families, and show itself not by actual fits but by violent periodic attacks of temper or other aggressive behavior. In some cases this can be modified by drugs or endocrine preparations. Heredity and the whole question of inherited patterns of behavior is a very complicated matter. Fortunately it is generally agreed that of the two, environment is the more important; it is at any rate something that we can hope to modify. It is found by research that in cases where heredity has been considered to be the chief factor, there have been influences in the very early development and upbringing which are the truer explanation of later difficulties in behavior. It is also true to say that even where there seem to be inherited tendencies, even to such serious conditions as schizophrenia, it is the early upbringing—the degree of love and security—which determines whether that tendency will come out or not. On the other hand, we know, too, that the effects of early deprivation of love and security may be so severe as to impoverish or distort the personality as much as, or more than, would any inherited taint. But this again is but a challenge to us to accept what is given, and measure ourselves against it with all the resources which our ever increasing knowledge gives us and with all the tireless devotion that we can command.

What we find in effect among these children is a breakdown in the process of control of the instinctive-emotional side of life. The familiar pattern is one where children are aggressive, demanding, acquisitive, restless, selfish, jealous, and moody. The instinctive control may be so poor that it is shown also in enuresis and encopresis, and in excessive greed. With all this, which is only one side of the picture, they are lively, responsive, amusing and lovable. But some remain moody, dejected and unapproachable for a long time.

Some are almost intolerable even to the most devoted and tolerant workers among them! There are those who have received such grievous psychic hurts that they take a very long time to heal, and indeed may never become quite whole. Those who have retreated from rather than reacted against the troubles in their lives are the more serious problem than the lively aggressive ones; and they may be the less noticed in schools or institutions. It must be realized however that all these characteristics of seriously disturbed children will reveal themselves only if permitted to do so, as I shall try to explain in the next section.

TREATMENT

The schools to which seriously maladjusted children are sent are generally organized for about thirty. A smaller number might be preferable, but uneconomic. If of the Hostel type, i.e. where the children go out to school, they can be smaller. Whether they should be of mixed sexes, and of what ages, is a vexed question. They should resemble a family, but it is an artificial family and brings its difficulties. As always there are pros and cons on both sides, but we cannot embark on this issue, which is too controversial to be considered here.

Treatment consists in the main of the impact made upon the child by the new environment in which he finds himself. This means the community or school as a whole, including the place, the staff, the pets, lessons, arts and crafts, outings, committees of children, and all manner of things. It also includes the parents and the home: visits, letters, holidays, talks with the staff, home visits by a social worker or teacher, all are essential. From the first moment the child is being prepared to return home, and the home itself is being almost insensibly prepared to receive back a "reformed" child.

This treatment is termed officially, "Special educational treatment." This is true only in the broadest terms. Lessons are certainly not the main feature, and everything that happens is educative or the reverse. Some of the children cannot, or will not, at first, take part in ordinary lessons, and it is useless, and sometimes harmful to make them do so.

The spirit of the place is what counts for most, and this is the creation almost entirely of those who are in charge; those who represent the "parental figures" to the children. This is true of course of all good schools. There are certain elements in that spirit, and in the method of working, which seem to be generally agreed upon at the present day, and in different countries.

TOLERANCE

It is obvious, or at any rate it has been learned by experience, that to impose a rigid discipline, or to adopt a spirit of disapproval and condemnation, is fatal to eventual success; the children must be allowed to reveal their natures, their aggression, and their particular forms of disturbance, whatever form—whether violent, "wicked" or "immoral"—it may be taking at the moment.[1] There are of course necessary limits, i.e. violence or harm to others has to be checked. Tolerance is a different thing to mere indifference: it means understanding, patience, tact and humor; it means knowing when to begin to apply that measure of control which will enable the child to be relieved of the anxiety produced by its own aggression, and to be helped to begin to acquire self-control. Things like swearing, wildness, sex-play, may be very trying, and shocking to our sense of what is right; but they are symptoms, which must not be driven underground. As the child becomes adjusted they should lessen; if we merely suppress them strictly we are not curing the child.

So far as possible the lessening of disorder and the promotion of order should come about by complete friendliness and co-operation between children and adults; it will be found that, given the chance, the children themselves show a deep understanding of each other's difficulties and failings, and of how to create as it were organs of government and discipline within their apparently anarchic group. "Committees", "Councils", "Ministries", or whatever name may be chosen, can be valuable means in promoting self-government and a sense of community.

Tolerance does not exclude punishment. In any case

[1] *Editor's note:* the author's attitude here is morally and psychologically correct in the Clinic with emotionally disturbed children, but normal children in the home need the threat of pain and punishment at times to help them control their behavior.

many actions bring their own punishment; unsocial actions bring social ostracism; abuse of a privilege involves loss of that privilege. Punishment may thus follow automatically, it may be ordered by an adult, or it may be decided by the children themselves with the sanction of an adult. In any case it is not a matter of rules but of handling an individual child by a particular adult in a special circumstance; it is a matter of the wisdom of the person who is in a position to administer, sanction, or withhold it. Punishment in general should be a means of restitution whether of something destroyed or stolen or of an order disturbed. It is certainly a very different concept from that found in most of the homes and some of the schools from which these children come, where punishment generally means being hit.

PERSONAL RELATIONSHIPS

Maladjusted or deprived children generally speaking have a craving for affection, which to them implies a physical demonstration of it. When they first come to a place where they receive this kind of affection, they may be insatiable in their demands to be cuddled and kissed and played with; they will behave like much younger children, or else precociously more like adults (I am speaking here of children between the ages of, say, nine and twelve). They have missed the stage of infancy with the warmth and tenderness of a mother's normal affection, or they have had it in brief and violent bursts. They are therefore possessive and jealous, and their love easily turns to hate because it has not known a gradual unfolding, and they have not experienced its tenderness. Some of them, too, will have witnessed or heard scenes of adult sexual life, or have been stimulated to feel a precocious urge for sensual satisfaction. Those who deny the capacity of quite young children for a close simulation of adult sexual experience are simply unaware of it, because they have not perceived it, or because they do not want to believe it.

The emotional relationship of such children to the adult is therefore a dangerous force and a difficult one for some adults, unless very balanced and experienced, to cope with. It has to be accepted and used; but it must be controlled and gradually diverted or sublimated. In some very "modern" schools the demands for love may be met too readily, and the relationship becomes too near an erotic one. The inexperienced enthusiastic student or worker may unwittingly fall into this danger. (It is also unfortunately true that this type of work does attract a type of unbalanced mind which seeks satisfaction in contact with children to compensate for their own failure in love.)

This excessively demonstrative type of relationship should become modified and develop into warm friendship, without being too possessive, leading to a secure trustfulness based on common interests and easy relationship. After all, in a normal family a measure of reasonable yet warm affection which is not—or should not be—sloppy or sentimental is expected, and a Home should try to approximate to a real home as closely as is possible.

The other extreme is of course equally bad, in fact worse. (The happy mean in anything is so hard to come by, it helps to depict extremes.) It is not necessary to discuss instances where there is deliberate harshness or even mental cruelty because we are not discussing the type of Institution where such things are likely, but there are Homes of an old-fashioned type where some of the children will certainly be maladjusted because deprived of normal family life, where the need of affection and of warm personal relationship is not even thought of. There may be a distant and austere relationship, or a rigid repressive discipline, so that the children are made "good" by force. There may also be an attempt to lead affection into religious channels without the mediation of human love. As a wise theologian put it: "Love of God is learnt through love of the mother"; one cannot promote a supernatural relationship without a natural basis: a child will not love Our Lord or His Mother, unless he loves the person who teaches him that love.

ACTIVITIES

There is a tendency to talk of personal relationships as though they existed in a vacuum. In other words to regard such relationships as holding between two individuals, or between various individuals, in the field of emotion irrespective of where they are and what they do together. This attitude or way of thinking seems to me to be responsible for the situation mentioned in the previous section, where the relationship drifts into an erotic and "unhealthy" type.

In actual fact, relationships are expressed and lived through in the day-to-day activities and duties of life, in shared interests, in work and in play. Life is not mainly a question of relationships in the sense of "feelings" between persons, but involves a third element: a discourse, a pleasure, a creation of something —whether it is a game, a song, a lesson, or what you will. With children this is most particularly the case. They need to be kept busy; many maladjusted children are hyperkinetic, which means that they are restless and "always on the go." If they have nothing to do, they indulge in aimless endless play, or just plain fooling, which whips them up to more activity, until they end up tired and fretful. The importance of creative activity is very great. Anyone who works with maladjusted children should be trained thoroughly in some craft, art, or interest which can be taught and enjoyed with the children. The capacity of children for making, doing, collecting is inexhaustible: but this needs the materials, the opportunity and the guidance to foster it, and give it effective expression.

This does not mean that all their activities are to be guided and controlled all the time; they must have time to roam about, to make dens, to indulge in their make-believe games, and so on. Often however it is found that, at first at any rate, these children do not know how to play, and cannot concentrate for long at anything; they tend to be endlessly repetitive, aimless, noisy or destructive, and have to be gradually led into more satisfying and constructive forms of activity.

To discover a child's particular talent or "grand passion" is often to find the key which unlocks the child's feeling; overcoming his inferiority, arousing his interest and spontaneity, putting him on the road to life.

7

Adolescence

A great many things can be said about adolescence which have often been said before, and are known to all of us who have to deal with young people at an age which is so full of paradoxes. Adolescents are both generous and selfish; they are rigid, and yet fluid and changeable; they are cynical yet full of ideals and romance; they are reaching intellectual and moral maturity, yet they may revert to the most childish moods and activities. They are both charming and detestable!

This is understandable enough if we remember that they are both child and adult together. They have lost the stability of the "gang age" (that is, between say seven and eleven), they are becoming conscious of a separate individuality which is very unsure of itself; in some ways their childhood is active once more: they are swayed by emotions that have their roots in infancy. We need not mention in addition the changes in their physical state, and the stirrings of sexual desire with all the difficulties which that may bring.

There is a kind of idea prevalent that there is inevitably some form of emotional disturbance at puberty, which is brought on by changes in the endocrine glands which occur at this stage. Now puberty is a natural process in growth, and if accepted naturally, there is no reason why it should create such a difficult phase. In some societies there seems to be no particular problem about adolescence, and in ours the amount of disturbance depends on the attitude taken towards the adolescent by the adults round him.

There is one aspect of physical growth which may however cause trouble. This is where physical development occurs too early or too rapidly, or where, on the contrary, it is too long delayed. Also where the different aspects of development—physical, intellectual, or emotional—do not synchronize. Thus we have the hulking boy or girl who looks two or three years older than he or she actually is, whose "mental age" is below the average and whose character may be infantile. It is easy for such to get into trouble.

In general however it is the attitude towards adolescents, both in the family and in society generally, which makes their passage to manhood easy or difficult. It is possible to suppress the urges towards more independence and responsibility; to keep a budding adolescent in such a state of dependence on parental sanctions, as to create a feeling of frustration and despondency. A continual atmosphere of disapproval of the aspirations, whims, prejudices and absurdities of the adolescent may produce a rebellious, negative, and hating attitude.

On the other hand puberty may usher in a phase of growing-up, where difficulties are outgrown, when fresh possibilities emerge and a fresh phase of companionship is possible.

To encourage this we need a great deal of tolerance, and must accept and take seriously many things which may seem to us either rather silly or not what we would wish for them. For example, their preoccupation with dress, and their attempts at adornment following a phase when they did not care how they looked, or whether they were even clean; their boy and girl friendships, and affairs, so often with members of the opposite sex, of which we have to pretend to approve. There are times, too, when they just lounge about, when they are dissatisfied or negative about everything. This phase may be likened to a field that is lying fallow, waiting for new growth.

Adolescence brings perhaps greater potential dangers to mental health than other ages, but it has also greater possibilities of adjustment than most, because it is a plastic and responsive age.

DIFFICULT DEVELOPMENT

There is one danger however which is pertinent to mental health in a narrower sense. I refer to the shadow of schizophrenia, a mental disorder which generally starts in late adolescence, but of which the warning signs may come sooner. This condition is essentially a withdrawal from reality, which leads gradually to a state of complete alienation from normality and fragmentation of the personality. It seems probable however that there are many cases of slight schizophrenic phases in adolescence which may pass unrecognized, and may account for the failures in study, the bizarre behavior, the moods of depression, and the occasional suicides among students. An American psychiatrist, writing of these cases of early schizophrenia, which he considers to be very common, says of their first signs: "You should have detected a certain interference in his contacts with other human beings; a kind of vague somewhat puzzling withdrawal. Beyond this you would have likely detected nothing."

In any school, especially for higher education, an intelligent head teacher will refer to a psychiatrist cases of adolescents who are failing in some way, or suffering from ill-defined ill-health, fears, moods, etc. A head teacher who is not perceptive or one who thinks he knows best, will have his eyes shut to this kind of case—until it is too late. In my experience this condition is commoner among boys and especially those of high intelligence.

One of the commonest subjective symptoms is that of feeling strange, of having a sense of unreality. This was well described by a boy of 15 who was sent to me years ago because he had developed fears and worries. He said that at times he felt dazed. He would ask himself: What am I? What is it all about? He got better after a few months of attendance at a Child Guidance Clinic, and wrote to me after service in the Air Force; he said: "The symptoms which worried me as a youngster were feelings of vagueness—a sense of detachment—as though I were non-existent, or a spectator of life instead of taking part in it."

The symptoms which at first draw attention to these cases vary; there may be physical fatigue, often described as laziness, moods of depression are not uncommon, unsociability to an increasing degree, fear of school for no obvious reason. There is generally a lack of interest and lack of feeling both in work and still more in people. The chief characteristic could be described as "withdrawals." The following are actual descriptions of symptoms in three cases which were all of boys between 14 and 16 of high intelligence: "depressed, anxious, and withdrawn"; "under tension, memory disturbed, feeling unreal"; "phases of depression and fear, phases of unreality."

In these particular cases, as in others similar to them, the condition passed off in about three months, during which time they were under observation, receiving moral support, and protection from any undue strain—such as being forced to work—discussing their problems, sexual and other. They may be said to have passed through transient adolescent episodes which at least suggested early schizophrenia. It is of course difficult to assess the number of such cases, or to measure the result of such treatment as they receive; many may pass unnoticed, others may drift into chronic states of mild or severe schizophrenia. At any rate it can be claimed that it is worth bearing these possibilities in mind when dealing with adolescents of this type.

There is another type of case among boys where the chief feature is an exaggerated "sensitivity." They are sometimes referred for advice on account of a fear of school which amounts to an acute phobia, and which may get them into trouble for not attending school. They are at a pre-pubertal stage, as a rule, when they break down, and they all tend to be of delicate, rather feminine type, timid and silent with strangers, often artistic or musical. They are unduly dependent on the mother, who over-protects them (with a consequent danger of homosexuality developing). It is easy to see that they will be called "sissy" and become the butt of their fellows. Fortunately, if adequate help and understanding are given, they will tend to improve with the onset of physical adolescence.

In girls we find rather different types of reaction: there are the hysterical types, and the overgrown precocious and aggressive ones. It is obviously not possible to enumerate all the difficult cases that may be met with towards the approach of puberty and after it. Most of them may be said to depend on some temporary disorder in growth, due to endocrine disfunction, so that the physical side is not keeping step, as it were, with the emotional, and vice versa. To these Dr. Marañon, an eminent Spanish doctor, has applied the useful term of "chronopathy", implying a temporary disorder of growth. We may be hopeful therefore, even when we get alarming outbreaks in our adolescents, that, with understanding, kindness, and tolerance, they will come through.

8

Conscience, Habits and Discipline

BEGINNING OF CONSCIENCE

It can be accepted that all human beings are born with at least the possibility of an active "conscience", which may be described in the terms: "I must love what is good and hate what is bad." It can also be accepted that a conscience is not a separate little department or control box in the mind which whispers to us, as it were, what we must and must not do, but that the adult, full, conscience is simply Reason in action, or the instructed Reason acting on the Will.[1]

It is also important to realize that part of the "conscience" is an aspect of the mind which develops from infancy, and is laid down in various layers as it were. What is "good" for the infant at first is the milk, and the breast, or the mother who provides it; what is "bad" is the absence of milk or the mother who seems to deprive him of it. It can then be supposed that the conflict between love and hate, and the feeling of hav-

[1] The extreme example of the idea that the "voice of conscience" is something apart, is found of course in the mental illness known as paranoia, where the patient actually projects this voice outside himself, and "hears voices."

ing hated what is good, namely the mother, produces a primitive kind of guilt: the conscience begins to form. Later this conflict of feelings, good and bad, is extended to all sorts of situations. The commands, prohibitions, and attitudes of the parents are absorbed as it were by the child's mind. But it is not just a case merely of accepting the explicit points of view of the parents: the parental figures are taken in as reflected in the child's mind and therefore in a distorted or exaggerated form. They may appear far more harsh and punitive than they are in fact, and also more omnipotent and loving. This can be seen in children's make-believe games; and also in the attitude of some grown-ups towards their parents! What may appear to be a theoretical (and very incomplete) account of the formation of this primitive conscience (in psychological terms the "Super-ego") has in fact very practical applications. Some people are harassed all their lives by morbid and irrational feelings of guilt. Others appear to be devoid of a moral sense. In the case of the latter—the so-called psychopathic individuals—it is found that there has been a profound disturbance in the mother-child relationship in early life: either it has been virtually non-existent or it has been disturbed and perhaps destroyed. Consequently such children grow up unable almost to have any relationship in an emotional sense with others, and can develop no feeling for the community.

To assist as far as possible in the formation of a "reasonable conscience" with an adequate sense of guilt when we do wrong, but free to a large extent from the primitive superstitious and morbid elements of the "Super-ego", is one of the most important tasks of parents and educators. The conscience, to the Christian who believes in freedom, is the final arbiter of belief and action, and so to understand its formation and its nature is of great importance.

HABITS

The formation of conscience is obviously bound up with questions of discipline, punishment, and with habits, i.e. the conduct of everyday life. To take first the question of habit-training: it might be thought that the earlier and more thoroughly we form good habits, e.g. of tidiness, cleanliness, obedience, etc., in the very young, the better for all concerned. It certainly makes life simpler in later years if we have grown up with good habits of this kind, but it can certainly be overdone, and end by having the opposite result. It is found, for example, that if infants are trained too early and too thoroughly to be clean, by lengthy sojourns on the pot, accompanied by much coaxing, and even scolding, they may break down later and start soiling or wetting. You cannot train human infants just as you do puppies: they are much more complicated in their emotional reactions.

If you insist too early and too much on obedience, good manners, and so on, you may turn out little slaves to good habits, who will be cowed, rigid and anxious children later, or else will become rebellious and difficult to handle. Freedom, spontaneity, and natural friendliness, are very precious things in childhood, not to be quenched by an excess of prohibitions, commands, and sanctions. The training of children must naturally be adapted to their age and their capacity to take it in. If overdone, it will sap their self-confidence, make them rebellious, deceitful, and hypocritical. You find such types in old-fashioned institutions, where this rigid training is still carried on. At the same time, the pendulum towards licence, away from obedience, can swing too far, and result in a chaotic, messy, egoistic, and unpleasant existence for everybody.

The problem of how to be happy though human, involves order: a certain degree of regularity and repetition in daily life, subordination to the comfort of others, even tidiness. Nature, after all, is regular and tidy in her operations; the creative artist is tidy and careful with his tools; you cannot make good food in a messy kitchen. Without regular habits, which can only be really acquired when young, much time is wasted, and a lot of irritation caused all round. So once again the moral is that we must try to achieve the happy mean.

This matter of training has been put neatly and simply by Fr. F. H. Drinkwater, as follows:

Many good Catholic mothers, or other rulers of nurseries, who love their children and are anxious to bring them up well, make sad mistakes in the process. "Don't do that, it's naughty" they will say when the child is making some quite innocent exploration of his world such as examining a kitchen knife for the first time; evidently this is going to confuse his ideas of right and wrong. The child probably asks "why?" and as likely as not the mother answers "because I tell you not to", thereby laying another stone in the foundation of an arbitrary morality, which being authoritarian rather than authoritative, is likely to be repudiated in later years. I think one should give a child brief reasons, often he will not understand them at all, but his personal dignity will be satisfied.

Some parents seem to view this behavior-training process as entirely a matter of obedience. Obedience has its place in human life, an important place, but that is just why it needs to be taught in a way that will last a lifetime. To reduce all conduct in early childhood to a matter of obedience is surely fatal. "Mummy won't love you if you do that" is another fatal mistake educationally. It is also of course a downright lie in itself, but small children may believe it and feel anxious and insecure. "You don't love mummy" is almost as bad, and "Jesus won't love you" is a good deal worse. All these blundering habits are frequent, and sometimes repeated from one generation to another. Often they are joined to a nervous fearfulness which leads parents to multiply needless prohibitions that either communicate their fear to the child, or else provoke it to constant revolt. The wise parent manages things so that clashes of will do not happen.[1]

DISCIPLINE

There are many shades of opinion of course with regard to discipline and a great deal of harm can be done by mistaken notions on the subject. There are certain aspects which may be called platitudes, such as the injunction to avoid extremes, to exercise absolute consistency ("always carry out what you say you are going to do"), and so on. These elementary notions certainly need to be driven home to parents and

[1] *The Tablet,* Sept. 19, 1953.

others, but here I would prefer to discuss the subject in more general terms.

Ideas on the subject spring from two sources: one is the tradition of the time and place in which people grow up, that is, the particular culture which influences them, both consciously and unconsciously. The other is the personal factor, that is, the intelligence, the degree of sensitivity or its opposite, the character as molded by the life experience from infancy onwards, of the individual.

There is nothing absolute about methods of discipline. The type of discipline which is right for the soldier in the Army, or for a nun or priest in convent or monastery, is not suitable for children. This sounds obvious, but I have come across a good few cases where it was unrealized or ignored. Some fathers back from the wars have adopted the methods of sergeant-majors at home. Some people seem to expect a degree of obedience and submission from small children which is monastic; and they can be harsh and unloving in promoting it. Nothing seems to me so terrible as mental or physical cruelty inflicted—even with the best intentions—upon helpless children in institutions. Yet this may happen, maybe, from a sense of duty, but also from unconscious evil promptings in the very depths of that person's mind and heart. This kind of harshness—a kind of perverted love—can arise from a misunderstanding of the idea of original sin. In a crude form this idea could be stated as follows: children, in common with human nature, are inherently "bad", and it is this which mainly causes them to be naughty, disobedient, lazy, etc. This tendency must be checked and beaten out of them if necessary until they submit and become "disciplined" into a semblance of good behavior; their "wicked little wills" must be mastered. Do these good people suppose that Christ had this kind of idea about children when he set one in the midst of them and uttered those immortal words about childhood?

Perhaps a great deal of the abuse of "discipline" would be avoided if one is imbued with the idea of "disciple". A child is your disciple, willing and free, if you are a worthy master. This is not to say that you can never be stern or even angry, but there must be love as a basis, which must be warm and tender too.

The relation between love, freedom and discipline is well expressed in the following lines by a professor of education:

There is nothing mysterious about the sequence in which love creates freedom, freedom is abused, and love again is needed to redeem the misuse of freedom. If it is the theme of the universe, it is also the theme of the family, and every mother knows it is true. Where there is no love, freedom is not given, because it is always less trouble not to give freedom.

Only love undertakes the anxiety and responsibility of giving freedom. It is inevitably abused, because we have to learn how to use it, and until we have learned, we are irresponsible, destructive, selfish, and inconsiderate . . . and in the long run only more love can win back the heart (not only the outward behavior) of the selfish and destructive to considerate responsibility. This is both homely experience and sound Christian doctrine.[1]

[1] Professor Jeffreys in *Glaucon*, p. 116.

9

Education and Mental Health

The school side of childhood problems is, strictly speaking, the work of the psychologist. When dealing with maladjusted children in a Child Guidance team, it is the educational psychologist naturally who deals with the intellectual and emotional aspects of the child's school life: his difficulties with learning, either general or in special subjects, and his attitude to school, teachers, etc. It is he who visits the schools and discusses the various problems, arranges for remedial teaching at the clinic, and so on.

But it must always be stressed that this work with maladjusted children is not in watertight compartments, far from it, and each member must know a good deal about the work and methods of the others. The psychiatrist must consider the educational side as an important part of the child as a whole, especially as so many difficulties of this kind depend on questions of health, temperament, and general hygiene. For example, some special difficulties in reading and writing may originate in some slight degree of damage to the brain at birth or after, causing lack of co-ordination between the brain centres and the muscles of expression.

The time has gone by, one hopes, when a child who is not doing well at lessons is merely described as "lazy", without any attempt to discriminate between the various conditions which might be keeping him back: lack of intelligence to start with, irregular growth perhaps, with endocrine disturbance; even insufficient sleep through bad home conditions; not to mention inadequate, harsh, or uninspired teaching, which bears so hardly on the dull child especially.

Some of the cases which should be spotted by a teacher as requiring expert investigation, are those where there is a failure to learn, which does *not* arise from dullness of intelligence. One has even come across cases which were considered to be so mentally retarded as to require education in a school for educationally subnormal children, and yet whose intelligence was well above normal.

One boy of nine was investigated for falling behind in his work, and especially for his extreme slowness. His intelligence was actually well above the normal, but he was suffering from a form of depression—a rare condition in childhood—which slowed down all his thought processes. Behind this lay a family history of mental illness, and certain emotional tension in the home. After fairly lengthy treatment at a clinic his depression passed off with some suddenness, and he managed to get into a Grammar School to which he has stood up very well. Coaching alone would not have helped in this case.

Such cases, where the use of the intelligence is inhibited or obscured by emotional disturbance, may be few; but it is very important that teachers should be able to spot them.

There is another condition which, though rare, it is important to recognize and seek advice about: this is school phobia. We are all familiar with children, of varying types and degrees of intelligence, who develop a dislike of school, fear of a particular teacher, a tendency to play truant or a refusal to go to school. Most of these should yield to the usual methods of adjustment. There are however certain cases where an acute neurotic fear, a kind of panic reaction, develops; where the anxiety takes on an extreme and compulsive quality. These children often try and get to school and can be seen to go pale, tremble and even vomit. They are usually "only" children who are over-dependent on their mothers. They are mostly boys, of a particular temperamental or physical type and often of high intelligence. The distinguishing feature is sensitivity. The trouble is not so much fear of school (once in school they are often all right) but a fear of leaving the sheltering wings of home. Such cases may respond to psychiatric treatment, but in some it may prove necessary to teach them at home or in very small groups (as is done for physically handicapped children).

(There are other cases of school failure in intelligent children, especially at puberty, which may foreshadow the onset of schizophrenia: I have mentioned these in the chapter on adolescence.)

These examples will show that there is a variety of cases showing difficulties at school who should be seen by a psychiatrist. They may be only passing phases of difficult adjustment, connected perhaps with the changes of puberty, worry over sex, etc., and will right themselves with growth. On the other hand they may signify the onset of serious mental disturbance. They will be helped in any case from the understanding and support of someone who is neither parent nor teacher.

EDUCATION

These are special problems connected with education in schools, but of course education is something much wider, and anyone concerned with mental health must have general ideas about education in general. The psychological pundits are fond of maintaining that psychiatrists lack the knowledge of normal children. They forget that we are also ordinary parents and citizens, and that as doctors we are equally interested in healthy bodies as in ill ones; therefore likewise in healthy and beautiful minds. One cannot help, even as a mere citizen, having views about education, seeing where the results seem to be bad as well as good, lending one's voice in support of what one feels strongly enough are the good trends in the process of educating the children of one's generation.

It is held, in the Christian tradition at least, that education is primarily and basically the function and responsibility of *parents*, though they may, and in practice must, delegate this function to teachers. This is not only the natural law, but the safeguard against all forms of State indoctrination and uniformity. It is usually forgotten. Those who uphold this principle should encourage parents to assume a vital interest in what their children are taught, how and why, through means such as parent-teacher associations, talks and discussions for parents, etc. Actually a great deal of good is done by the informal chats of head teachers (in day schools) with individual parents, and the good head teacher knows a great deal about the home background of his or her charges, and can do much good in a quiet way.

From the point of view of mental health then, one should ask in what way is education to-day on the wrong course, or not developing sufficiently along the way that one feels to be best? In the first it would seem that in the higher reaches of education, that is in Grammar Schools, Public Schools (and later the Universities) the intensity of learning is still increasing, and has been stepped up more and more. Every subject tends to be taught at a specialist level, e.g. the endless details to be learned about unimportant periods in History, the study of books obviously beyond the grasp, intellectual or emotional, of boys and girls of the age at which they are presented to them. The strain and the competition involved are becoming too great. It seems to be agreed that this process is to be laid at the door of University professors; but nothing seems to get done about it.

What appears however to me to be the chief failure right through education is that the effect is not continued to any extent beyond school-life. It is not only that school subjects are dropped with a sigh of relief as soon as schooling is over (with exceptions of course), but that the majority of children leave school without any sense of values. Their capacity for appreciation, or criticism, of what is worth reading, listening to, looking at, is on the whole lamentable. This surely cannot be denied. More, their power to express themselves in speech, reading or discussing, and still more in writing, seems at a very low level; especially where the dull children coming from inadequate homes are concerned.

ART IN EDUCATION

Where there is a living cultural tradition, with folk art, music and religion, there is a real education in living, in vital expression, though there may be few who can even read. The problem is how to revive some form of culture which is better than that of the cheap press, the American Comic, and other means of uncreative occupation. Have we perhaps found the answer in the discovery of child art in its various forms, in the discovery, for it is something new in education, that children have a capacity for design, color, movement, mime, and making things, which is as it were a source of renewal hitherto hardly used? The idea, I need hardly say, is not mine. The method may be termed "Education in Things" or "Education through Art". I quote these ideas from two writers whose work I have found an inspiration.

Eric Gill, a sculptor who also wrote about the things that were lacking in our modern society, was wont to say that we had education: first of the intellect, that is ideas, facts, letters and figures; secondly of the will or character by means of games; but where was there any education in *things?* That is, in the things that pertain to the senses: in colors and sounds and materials; in creation and craftsmanship.

Herbert Read, poet, critic, and philosopher, has supplied us with a book of great importance in his *Education through Art*. A later book, *Education for Peace* [1] puts these ideas in shorter form, and in relation to the problems of peace and war (which overshadow all our ideas, hopes, and plans to-day). I quote the following:

I advocate a reform in education which puts art where it should always have been—right in the heart of things. Let us begin with the primary schools. If we can reform our methods of teaching, and our attitude towards the objectives of education, so that some native sensibility is preserved in children, and children are no longer brutalized and anaesthetized by the bludgeoning process of learning—that is to say, hammering conceptual knowledge into their innocent minds—then there would be some human material to work with. You can't make the silk purses of art with the sow's ears of school certificates. You can't expect the flowering of the creative instinct in an epoch which condemns its children to the *via dolorosa* of examinations.

[1] Published by Kegan Paul, 1950.

This may sound a somewhat violent statement, and is obviously intended to arouse a fairly violent reaction. It will be said that the lessons which this and other statements propound, have already been accepted and applied in the best modern schools. It is true that many Education authorities are aware of the importance of Art, not just as an extra "subject" but as an important and integral part of education. As Eric Gill put it, "We don't want children to think of art as being only pictures and such. We want them to think of it as the exercise of skill and imagination in *every* department of human work". [1]

The method of education is certainly widening in the direction of creativity as well as learning, of doing as well as thinking; some people think it is going too far. But there are still many schools, especially on the Continent, where there persists too intellectualist an approach; where the imagination and critical judgement are insufficiently nourished. To educate means to nourish as well as to draw out, but not the intellect alone, rather the personality as a whole.

This applies most pertinently to religious education. The religion which we serve, which we believe to be the basis of education and of life, is embodied and expressed in every kind of Art and Symbol. If we as Catholics regard the Faith as the very foundation of mental health for the human race, we must be enabled to grasp and to hold it, at every stage of life, in all its riches and fullness.

[1] *Last Essays,* p. 56.

Conclusion

It would seem well to conclude with a brief summary of the views which I have tried to express in this book, so that the threads may be gathered up into a coherent pattern.

We are dealing with maladjustment: its varieties and causes, the main lines of its treatment and prevention, with some hints of its setting in the life of our day. We are concerned with the individual child who inherits, and acquires, personal characteristics, and with the environment—family, school, and culture—in which he develops.

The main factors which make for mental health, or for maladjustment—whether neurosis, anti-social behavior, or faults of character—may be listed as follows; remembering however that there is never a single cause, but a combination of circumstances at work:

1. The constitutional inherited "make-up", including the intelligence and the physical "type" and temperament. Thus the degree of sensitivity, of stability, and maturation in the nervous system, and of the body generally, at different ages, will help to determine

how the individual will respond to the environment.

2. The kind of upbringing and training. This means in effect a due balance between security and independence, between tolerance and control. The main fault is probably that of expecting too much. If too much is demanded in the way of achievement, obedience, keeping still, etc., etc., at the wrong age, the result may be a discouraged and "nervous", or a resentful and "difficult", child.

3. Traumatic events in the child's life. Deprivation of maternal care and affection in the early years is of course the most serious of these. This may be continuous, or temporary through absence in a hospital, etc. Illnesses, accidents, sexual experiences, may also act as "precipitating" causes. The arrival of siblings, without due preparation for this event, including adequate sex instruction, is a common starting point for difficulties.

The impact of school, fear of a teacher, or of rough companions, may also be mentioned.

4. Effects of parental character and attitudes. This may seem obvious, but it may not be fully realized to what extent children may become "identified" with the emotional problems of the parents, in an unconscious manner. Not only that the parents may be in a state of disharmony or disagreement, but that their own perhaps unconscious feelings of rejection, guilt, or jealousy, may be influencing the child, and causing symptoms which are not understood and appear causeless. The bringing to light and resolving of these conflicts is indeed one of the main tasks in the therapy of maladjustment.

The results of these events and circumstances are of course extremely varied, ranging from stomach-aches to violent tempers, from night-terrors to delinquency. Many of these manifestations are indeed "normal" and to be expected. There is no sharp dividing line between normal and abnormal, between mental health and neurosis. It is only at a certain degree of intensity and duration that symptoms will be said to constitute maladjustment. Different phases in health and behavior occur in all children; to recognize at what stage—when a phase is unduly prolonged, or when a child is unduly unhappy or disturbed—to seek expert help, is simply a matter of individual intelligence and judgement on the part of parent, teacher, doctor, or judge.

It is only in a few children that we find clear-cut examples of conditions which can be given a definite label, such as hysteria, obsessional neurosis, or schizophrenia; but it is vital that these children should receive immediate and effective treatment, if future failure or at worst disaster, is to be avoided.

The modern method of treatment of these conditions by the method generally known as Child Guidance has been described. It has been emphasized that it consists not only in adjustment or change of external factors—such as change of school, a different type of discipline at home, provision of outlets, etc.—but in a deeper type of therapy. This involves the elucidation of the more subtle and unconscious elements in the situation, and their resolution or modification; by weekly interviews with parents, and by treatment of the child with the techniques of child therapy. The latter include means of self-expression and the setting up of a relationship with the therapist, which results in some degree of self-understanding by the child, working through his "bad" feelings and his fears, establishing self-confidence, and achieving a relative freedom from useless and harmful emotions.

In some cases the unsuitability of the home background, and the hopelessly antagonistic situation between parents and children, render it necessary to treat the child away from home, for a period of one to three or more years. The conditions and the problems involved in this method of treatment have been outlined. The régime of such schools or hostels and the kind of relationship which should exist between staff and children, is of importance not only in schools for maladjusted children, but in Approved Schools and in Institutions for orphans or deprived children.

When we come to *prevention* of mental ill-health, crime, etc., we realize that curative methods by Child Guidance, etc., are not enough; that we have to start much earlier, and prepare young parents to acquire an easy, tolerant, understanding towards their progeny. Following from this, the elements of mental hygiene and child psychology must be taught to all those who deal with mothers and children in the complex State of to-day. Behind all this of course there are wider issues: of education, culture, religion; of Life itself. But we can all, in our different spheres and capacities, learn from our children, how to work for a happier and a better world.